My Baby
& Me

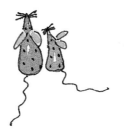

My Baby & Me

A Single Parent's Journal

for the first five years

Conceived and Written by Judith Levy

Illustrated by Sophie Allport

Stewart, Tabori & Chang
New York

Published in 1999 by

Stewart, Tabori & Chang

A division of U.S. Media Holdings, Inc.

115 West 18th Street

New York, NY 10011

Distributed in Canada by

General Publishing Company Ltd.

30 Lesmill Road

Don Mills, Ontario, Canada M3B 2T6

ISBN: 1-55670-890-4

Printed in Hong Kong

10 9 8 7 6 5 4 3 2 1

First Printing

dedication

Perhaps it's not conventional,
Or the way it used to be,
But it works for us together,
My baby, you and me.

With love for CRISTINA & JOSHUA

From NONNA

Date

Of all the joys that lighten suffering earth, what joy is welcomed like a new-born child?
—Caroline Norton

Of all nature's gifts to the human race, what gift has Providence bestowed on man that is so dear to him as his children?
—Cicero

. . . every baby born into the world is a finer one than the last.
—Charles Dickens

Wonderful!

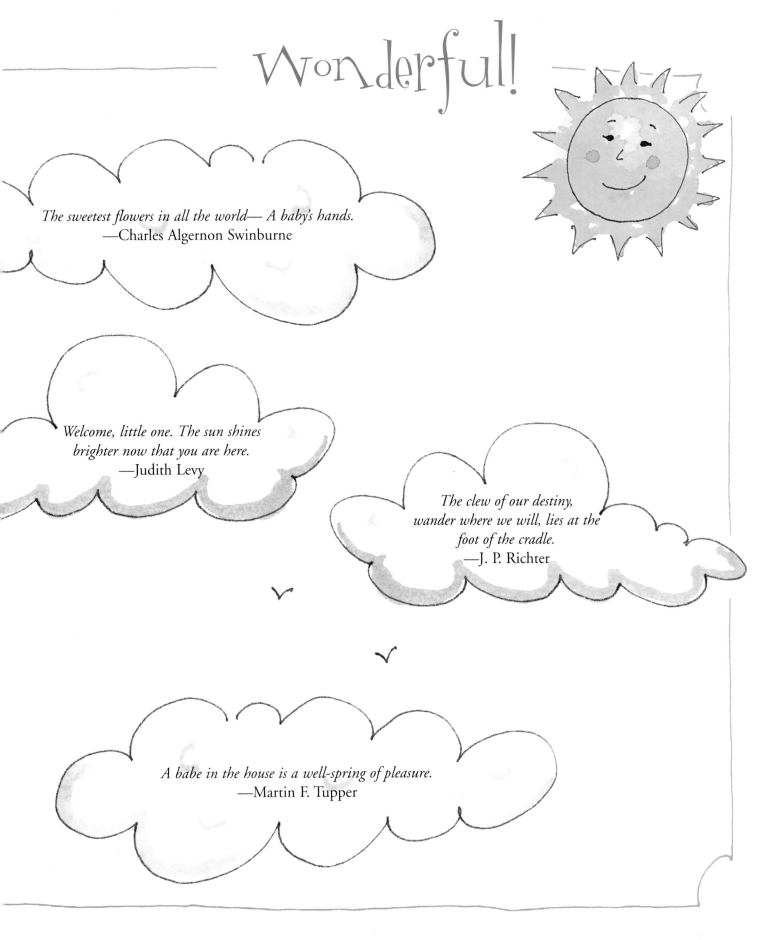

The sweetest flowers in all the world— A baby's hands.
—Charles Algernon Swinburne

Welcome, little one. The sun shines
brighter now that you are here.
—Judith Levy

The clew of our destiny,
wander where we will, lies at the
foot of the cradle.
—J. P. Richter

A babe in the house is a well-spring of pleasure.
—Martin F. Tupper

table of

contents

our family tree

Some trees have lots of branches
While others have a few,
But our branches are very sturdy,
And they're filled with love for you.

Me

My Baby

my grandparents

Paste photo here

Paste photo here

my grandparents

*It's a gift of the past
I'd like to unfold.
It's something more precious
Than rubies and gold.*

My Maternal Grandparents

Their names *DANILO V. SANTOS, M.D*

Their address *21 SILVER STIRRUP CT*
Timonium, MD 21093

My grandfather worked as *PHYSICIAN (OB/GYN)*

My grandmother worked as *Homemaker (later as a sales director for Marriott)*

My grandparents will always be special to me because

My Paternal Grandparents

Their names

Their address

My grandfather worked as

My grandmother worked as

My grandparents will always be special to me because

my parents

*Paste photo
here*

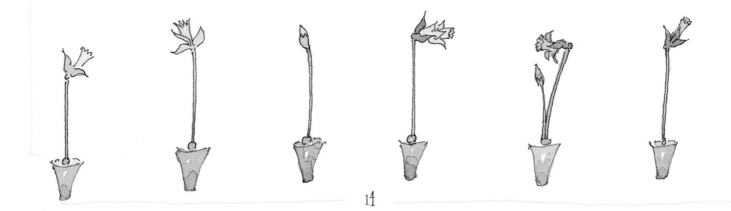

my parents

It wasn't always easy,
I frayed a nerve or two.
But when I counted on my parents,
They always came through.

My father's name _____

My mother's name _____

Their address _____

_____

My father worked as _____

_____

My mother worked as _____

_____

What I treasure most about my father is _____

_____

What I treasure most about my mother is _____

_____

_____

Introducing Me

*Paste photo
here*

Introducing Me

Take my hand and wander
Through yesterday, and then
I'll tell you how it used to be,
And enjoy it all again.

I was born on _____

Time _____

Place _____

_____

My name is _____

I was given this name because _____

_____

My weight _____

My length _____

Other members of my family are _____

_____

_____

When i was little

Paste photo
here

When i was little

My Favorites

Toy

Book

Actor

Actress

Movie

Television series

Rock group

Song

Trip

Food

Family Tradition

Holiday Tradition

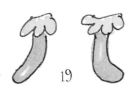

growing up

Paste photo here

growing up

Schools I attended were _____

_____

_____

_____

My best subject in school was _____

_____

I was never very good at _____

_____

A subject I grew to love was _____

_____

The teacher who influenced me the most was _____

_____

I'll always remember that teacher because _____

_____

growing up

Paste photo
here

growing up

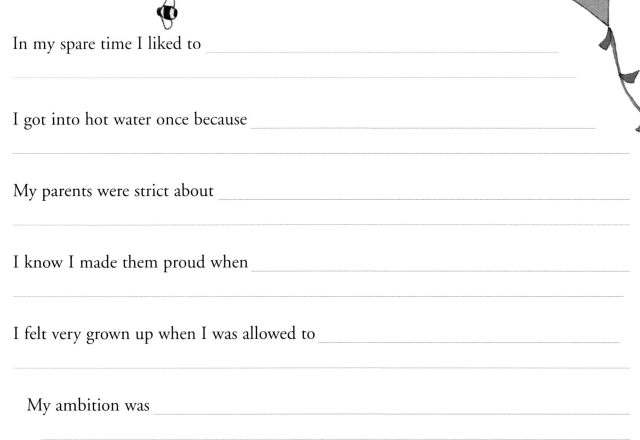

In my spare time I liked to _____

_____

I got into hot water once because _____

_____

My parents were strict about _____

_____

I know I made them proud when _____

_____

I felt very grown up when I was allowed to _____

_____

My ambition was _____

_____

My first job was _____

_____

introducing you!

*Paste photo
here*

introducing you!

My world's a nicer place,
The sun is shining through,
Happiness came to call,
All wrapped up in you.

I realized you were coming when _____
 _____
_____

My first reaction was _____
_____
_____

The first people I told were _____
_____
_____

I prepared by _____
_____
_____

I was happy because _____
_____
_____

*Paste invitation
or
photo here*

baby shower

While I was waiting
In happy anticipation,
There was a shower of love,
A baby celebration.

Date _____

Place _____

Given by _____

Guests   Favorite Gifts

_____

_____

_____

_____

_____

_____

_____

*Paste photo
here*

your birth day

Unbelievably tender,
Unbelievably sweet,
The joy you brought me
Made my life complete.

Your date of birth _____

Time _____

Place _____

Your weight _____

Your length _____

Your hair color _____

Your blood type _____

When I saw you for the first time I thought _____

_____

Your first visitors were _____

_____

_____

Everyone said you were _____

_____

a moment in time

Paste newspaper clipping here

a moment in time

*So much is happening
In my world, it's true,
But the best news of all
Is you, you, you!*

On the Day You Were Born

The local headlines were

_____

_____

The national headlines were

_____

_____

The world headlines were

_____

_____

The President of our country was _____

The important issues of the day were _____

_____

The weather was _____

A popular fad of the time was _____

_____

homecoming

*Paste photo
here*

homecoming

Off on your first trip,
Not too far to roam.
You're wrapped up in a blanket,
And we're ready to go home.

Date _____

We went home with _____

You and I lived at _____

The first night you slept in _____

I fed you every _____

Your disposition was _____

Your first visitors were _____

_____

I was concerned about _____

_____

I handled it by _____

_____

What I recall most about those first days is _____

_____

_____

_____

naming you

Paste photo
here

naming you

Which name to choose,
Lots I'm thinking of.
It's got to be perfect
For this child that I love.

Your name _____

Your name means _____

I chose your name because _____

Other people nicknamed you _____

My pet names for you were _____

What I remember most about naming you is _____

_____

_____

_____

important firsts

Paste photo
here

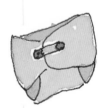

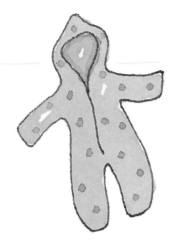

important firsts

How quickly you learn things,
Curious as you can be.
So smart and wonderful,
And such a joy to me.

You first slept through the night _____

Your first smile _____

You first rolled over _____

You first sat up unsupported _____

You first crawled _____

Your first tooth appeared _____

You first ate solid food _____

You first stood up _____

important firsts

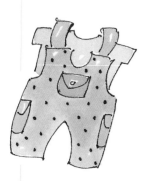

*Paste photo
here*

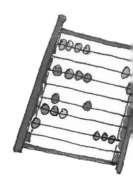

important firsts

You took your first steps _____

You first drank from a cup _____

You said your first word _____

You had your first haircut _____

Other important firsts:

_____

_____

_____

_____

_____

I was amazed when for the first time you _____

_____

_____

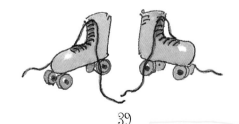

your average day

So many things to learn,
So many things to do.
In and out of everything,
My little genius, you.

You are up by _____

For breakfast you eat _____

_____

You love to play with _____

_____

When I must be away, the person who cares for you is _____

_____

Nap time is _____

For lunch you love to eat _____

_____

You break into a smile when _____

_____

I love it when you _____

_____

Bedtime is a special time because _____

_____

When I peek in at you while you are sleeping, I realize _____

_____

my average day

I juggle and I schedule,
The hours just slip through.
So many things go undone,
But there's always time for you.

I get up at _____

My day begins with _____

_____

Then I _____

_____

My day is filled with _____

_____

_____

I wish I had time for _____

_____

I eat dinner by _____

I finally go to sleep by _____

I consider it a good day when _____

_____

Our best time together is when we _____

_____

our Weekends

It would be nice to have
A peaceful day of rest,
With my feet on a pillow
And your head on my chest.

On Saturdays we usually _____

_____

_____

On Sundays we love to _____

_____

_____

Occasionally on a weekend we _____

_____

_____

The thing I like most about weekends is _____

_____

_____

My idea of a perfect weekend is _____

_____

_____

our first trips

You're a sturdy little traveler,
There's lots for you to see.
When I'm off for an adventure,
You come along with me.

On our first trip together, we traveled by _____

_____

We visited _____

_____

A toy we always took along was _____

_____

Your first plane ride was _____

_____

When we traveled we always played _____

_____

We had so much fun the time we went to _____

_____

_____

_____

_____

✳ bath time ✳

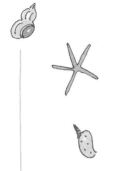

*Paste photo
here*

⋆ bath time ⋆

*I love to wash you in the tub
And get you squeaky clean.
You're the cutest little baby
That I have ever seen.*

You had your first bath at the age of _____

You were bathed in _____

_____

Your first reaction was _____

_____

_____

You graduated to the big tub _____

Your favorite water toy is _____

After the bath it is time to _____

_____

_____

Your bath time is fun because _____

_____

_____

_____

*Paste photo
here*

# first birthday

This year's been one of learning,
For me as well as you.
And we've passed with flying colors,
We're a winning team, we two.

We celebrated your birthday by _____
_____

You were happiest about _____

I was thrilled because _____

You received cards and gifts from _____
_____
_____

Your birthday cake was _____

When you saw your birthday cake, you _____

What I remember most about this year is _____
_____
_____

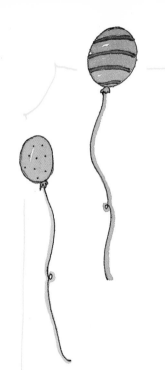

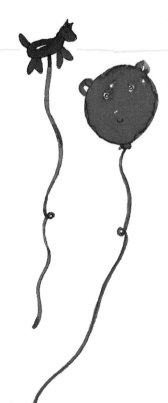

*Paste photo
here*

 Second birthday

Another year of growing
And problem solving too.
We're together and we're happy,
And it's all because of you.

Now that you're two years old you can _____

_____

You're very curious about _____

_____

It's almost impossible to keep you out of _____

_____

Your favorite food is _____

You refuse to eat _____

Your bedtime is _____

Your favorite toy is _____

Your favorite story is _____

Your favorite song is _____

You're afraid of _____

When you cry, the best way to comfort you is _____

_____

What I remember most about this year is _____

_____

_____

third birthday

*Paste photo
here*

 third birthday

I can't believe how quickly
The last three years have passed.
We faced it all together
And it all flew by so fast.

Now that you're three, you can _____

Your favorite activity is _____

Your favorite toy is _____

Your favorite story is _____

Your favorite song is _____

Your favorite food is _____

You always ask "why" about _____

You love to _____

You like to share _____

But you won't ever let go of _____

You never want to _____

Your favorite friend is _____

You always mispronounce _____ You say _____

We celebrated your birthday by _____
_____

We invited _____
_____

What I remember most about this year is _____
_____
_____

Paste photo here

fourth birthday

You're safe, you're loved, my four-year-old.
You needn't have a care.
You can count on me, my little one,
For, I always will be there.

Now that you're four you can _____

You're so independent about _____

I can always count on you to _____

You never want to _____

You love to _____

Bedtime is _____

Your favorite game is _____

Your favorite toy is _____

Your favorite book is _____

Your best friend is _____

You're happiest when _____

I laugh when you _____

_____

We celebrated your birthday by _____

_____

We invited _____

_____

What I remember most about this year is _____

_____

_____

fifth birthday

*Paste photo
here*

fifth birthday

We've been together for five years
And I've watched you grow.
You're a child of my heart,
And I love you so.

Now that you're five, you can _____

_____

You love to _____

You help me around the house by _____

_____

Your room can best be described as _____

You have good judgment about _____

You're sometimes naughty about _____

You're proud of _____

Your best friend is _____

You never want to _____

We celebrated your birthday by _____

_____

We invited _____

_____

What I remember most about this year is _____

_____

_____

School days

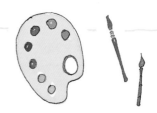

Preschool _____
Location _____
Teachers _____

Kindergarten _____
Location _____
Teachers _____

Grade School _____
Location _____
Teachers _____

Special Classes _____
Location _____
Teachers _____

School days

You're hurrying off to class
And I should have no fears.
You're such a big little person,
Still, I'm blinking back the tears.

On the first day of school, you _____

_____

You were always interested in _____

_____

I thought you might grow up to be _____

_____

Your favorite teacher was _____
Your favorite school friend was _____
In school you loved to _____

_____

I was so proud when your teacher told me that you _____

_____

holidays

*Paste photo
here*

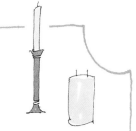

Holidays can be happy times,
And sometimes lonely too.
But each holiday has more meaning
Now that I have you.

Our First Holiday Together

Date

We shared this holiday with

What I remember most about this day

Another Holiday We Shared

Date

We shared this holiday with

What I remember most about this day

Another Holiday We Shared

Date

We shared this holiday with

What I remember most about this day

Another Holiday We Shared

Date

We shared this holiday with

What I remember most about this day

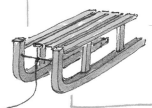

keeping you healthy

As a parent I worry
More than words can tell.
So we're off to the doctor
To keep you feeling well.

Your doctor's name _____

_____

Your first appointment was _____

_____

Your reaction to the visit was _____

Accidents

What happened _____

What happened _____

I knew you were sick when _____

If you were upset, I would comfort you by _____

For your medical history, it's important for you to know that _____

_____

So big

Oh yes, I can measure
Height and weight and such.
But how much do I love you?
You'd never guess how much.

	Height	Weight
Three months		
Six months		
One year		
Eighteen months		
Two years		
Three years		
Four years		
Five years		

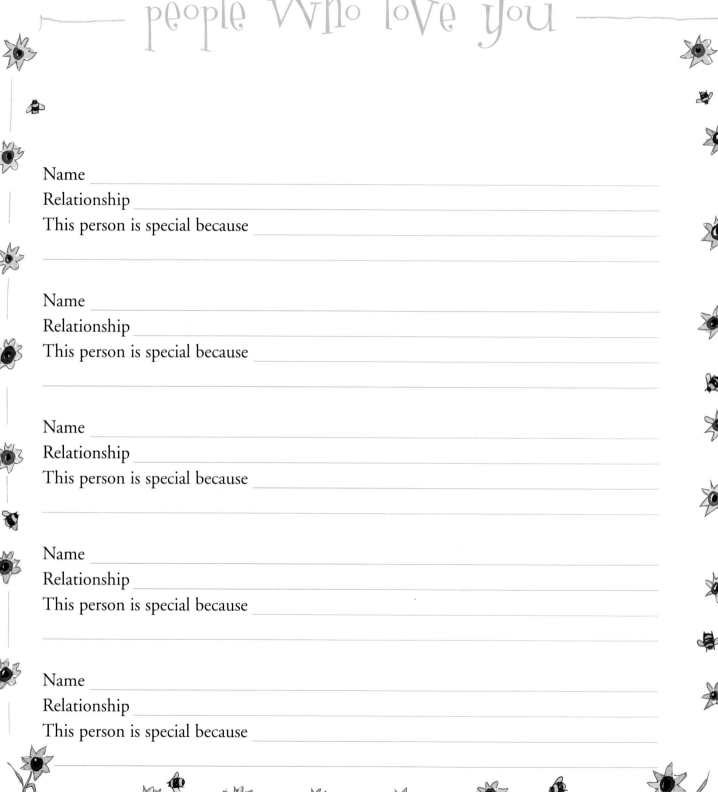

people who love you

Name _____

Relationship _____

This person is special because _____
_____

Name _____

Relationship _____

This person is special because _____
_____

Name _____

Relationship _____

This person is special because _____
_____

Name _____

Relationship _____

This person is special because _____
_____

Name _____

Relationship _____

This person is special because _____
_____

people who love you

Sometimes it's you and me,
And we don't need any more.
Other times we have such fun
With these people we adore.

Name _____

Relationship _____

This person is special because _____

_____

Name _____

Relationship _____

This person is special because _____

_____

Name _____

Relationship _____

This person is special because _____

_____

Name _____

Relationship _____

This person is special because _____

_____

Name _____

Relationship _____

This person is special because _____

_____

high hopes

If my fondest wishes
Could all come true,
I'd want peace for the world,
And happiness for you.

I hope your future is filled with _____

_____

_____

_____

_____